A Leopard book

Leopard Book of Bible Puzzles

by Colin Quayle

SCRIPTURE UNION
130 City Road, London EC1V 2NJ

First published 1977
Fourth reprint 1987

ISBN 0 85421 511 5

Printed and bound in Great Britain by
Cox & Wyman Ltd., Reading

Introduction

A closed book?

Many people do not understand the Bible: it is a closed book to them. If they open it at all, they become quite bewildered by the large number of strange names and titles. Sometimes this makes them decide that they are not interested.

Why puzzles?

One reason why I have written this book is because I think it is always great fun to do puzzles. Another reason is to give you the chance to practise using the Bible and to get to know some of the names and people in it.

A library

Before trying to solve the puzzles, open your Bible at the contents page, and look at the list of titles. Don't worry if you can't pronounce some of the names. Each of these names is the title of a separate book in the Bible: the Bible is really a collection of books, like a library. There are history books, poetry books, biographies, travel books and letters. All the books in the Old Testament were written before Jesus was born, and all the books in the New Testament were written after he died.

Finding the right page

When you read these puzzles and see a reference to a Bible book, look in the contents page of the Bible to find the page number where the book starts. Every book in the Bible is divided into chapters and verses. When you see

Genesis 20.1

it means Genesis chapter 20, verse 1. The big numbers at the top of every page and the big numbers in the margins, are the chapters. The small numbers in the margins or in the middle of the lines, are the verses.

1 Chronicles 5.23

means the first book of Chronicles, chapter 5, verse 23.

An open book?

Some of the puzzles are easy, some are more difficult. By the time you have solved them the Bible will no longer be a closed book to you. You will begin to find your way around the Bible.

Understanding the Bible

The books in the Bible teach us about God, about what he is like and about how we can get to know him. Some of the books in the Bible are easy to understand, but some are difficult. Scripture Union publish special booklets which help you to understand what the Bible passages mean. If you are aged 8 to 11 there is a booklet called QUEST NOTES, and if you are 11 to 14 you should get KEY NOTES. You can buy these at a Christian bookshop if there is one near where you live. Or you can write for information to Scripture Union, Mail Order Department, Clothier Road, Bristol BS4 5PS.

Translations

When the Bible was first written, the writers wrote in Hebrew or in Greek. The Bible you have is a translation from these languages. There are many different transla-

6

tions of the Bible. When I worked these puzzles out, I used the Authorized Version (this is also called the King James Bible) and the Revised Standard Version. When you are solving these puzzles, therefore, you need to use the AV (the Authorized Version) or the RSV (the Revised Standard Version). You can use either of these translations to get the right answer, except for a very few times, when you can only use one translation. When this happens I have told you in the puzzle which translation to use.

Colin Quayle

THE MAZE

The maze is one of the earliest puzzles. This one is a hedge maze and contains four arbours, each named after one of the Four Evangelists or Gospel-Writers. Your task is to find your way through the maze. You must visit each of the arbours in the order in which the names of the corresponding Gospels appear in the New Testament. Then, as there is only one entrance, you must find your way back to where you started. You may not use any path more than once.

IS IT GENUINE?

One day when Mark was digging in the garden his spade struck something hard. He picked up the hard object and washed it. It was a coin like this one:

'This coin was made just before Jesus was born,' he told his friend, Stephen. 'Augustus was the Emperor of Rome at that time. Perhaps it is a valuable coin. I'll take it into school and find out.'

Mark took the coin into school and showed it to Mr Barker, his teacher. Carefully, Mr Barker examined it.

'I'm very sorry, Mark,' said Mr Barker, 'but this isn't a real coin at all. I'm afraid that it's a forgery.'

How did Mr Barker know this?

CROSSWORD NO. 1

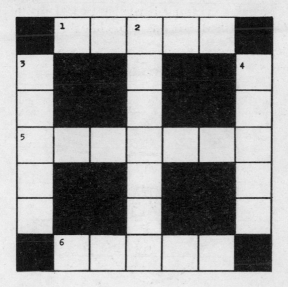

ACROSS

1. The 20th book of the New Testament (5)
5. He journeyed (7) (Genesis 20.1)
6. Jesus asked for a . . . . . (5) (John 4.7)

DOWN

2. The last book of the Old Testament (7)
3. A land which St Paul hoped to visit (5) (Romans 15.24)
4. He carried the cross for Jesus (5) (Luke 23.26)

CROSSWORD NO. 2

1. The 17th book of the Old Testament (6)
5. The 34th book of the Old Testament (5)
7. Pointed weapons (5) (Ephesians 6.17)
8. The 9th book of the Old Testament (6)

DOWN

2. A place near Mount Hermon (5) (1 Chronicles 5.23)
3. The 6th book of the New Testament (6)
4. The 2nd book of the Old Testament (6)
6. The king's business requires this (5) (1 Samuel 21.8)

A STRANGE STORY

MELASUREJ MORF NWOD GNIOG SAW NAM A
SREBBOR GNOMA LLEF EH DNA OHCIREJ OT
DNA, MIH TAEB DNA MIH DEPPIRTS OHW
DAED FLAH MIH GNIVAEL DETRAPED

This is the beginning of a very well-known parable
which Jesus told. It is not in a foreign language, but it
is written in an unusual way. Can you read it?

MOTHERS AND SONS

Who was the mother of:
(1) ISAAC   (Genesis 21.2–4)
(2) JACOB   (Genesis 25.28)
(3) JOSEPH   (Genesis 35.24)
(4) SAMUEL   (1 Samuel 1.20)
(5) SOLOMON   (1 Kings 1.11)
(6) JOHN THE BAPTIST
                   (Luke 1.57)

NAME-SEARCH

```
D  E  O  M  G  E  N  E
T  U  N  Y  S  U  I  S
E  R  O  L  O  D  S  N
T  I  V  E  X  B  M  U
I  C  U  S  E  E  R  S
```

Starting with the D in the top left-hand corner of the rectangle, you may move one space at a time upwards, downwards or sideways but never diagonally. Every letter in the rectangle is used only once.

You should find the names of five Old Testament books. What are the five books and what do they have in common?

PALINDROMES

Palindromes are words which are spelt the same backwards and forwards. For example, Eve is the first palindromic name in the Bible. Look up these references and you will find more people with palindromic names:

1 Samuel 1.2   1 Kings 15.8   Joshua 1.1
1 Chronicles 5.4   1 Chronicles 7.7   Luke 2.36

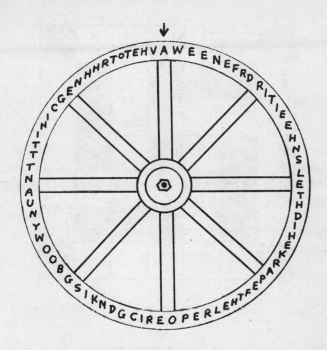

Start with the arrowed letter, miss three letters, read the fourth, and go on reading every fourth letter until you have been around the wheel five times and used every letter once.

By that time you will have a well-known verse from St Luke's Gospel. What does it say?

CROSSWORD NO. 3

ACROSS

1. The . . . . . of my hands (5) (Isaiah 49.16)
5. Town visited by St Paul (5) (Acts 16.8)
7. The 28th book of the Old Testament (5)
8. Buy it but do not sell it (5) (Proverbs 23.23)

DOWN

2. She named him . . . . . (5) (Exodus 2.10)
3. Aquila had come from this land (5) (Acts 18.2)
4. The 33rd book of the Old Testament (5)
6. A son of Joktan (5) (Genesis 10.29)

ALPHABET: PEOPLE OF THE
OLD TESTAMENT

Complete the alphabet by finding the names of people whom you read about in the Old Testament. You are given the first letter of each name, a short clue and a Bible reference to help you.

A......	Father of Isaac	(Genesis 21.3)
B.......	Joseph's brother	(Genesis 35.24)
C...	Murdered his brother	(Genesis 4.8)
D....	Son of Jesse	(Ruth 4.22)
E.....	Cured leprosy	(2 Kings 5.20)
G.....	Fought Midian	(Judges 7.14)
H.....	Mother of Samuel	(1 Samuel 1.20)
I....	Father of Esau	(Genesis 25.26)
J....	Brother of Esau	(Genesis 25.26)
K...	Father of Saul	(1 Samuel 9.1–2)
L..	Son of Haran	(Genesis 11.31)
M....	Brother of Aaron	(Exodus 4.14)
N...	Father of Shem	(Genesis 6.10)
O...	A King of Israel	(1 Kings 16.16)
P....	A King of Israel	(2 Kings 15.25)
R.....	Son of Jacob	(Genesis 35.23)
S.....	A very strong man	(Judges 16.30)
T.....	An Ammonite	(Nehemiah 4.3)
U....	Bathsheba's husband	(2 Samuel 11.3)
Z....	A priest	(2 Samuel 8.17)

CROSSWORD NO. 4

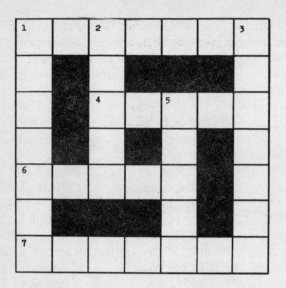

ACROSS

1. One of the women with Jesus (7) (Luke 8.3)
4. A city of Crete (5) (Acts 27.8)
6. The 28th book of the Old Testament (5)
7. The 4th book of the Old Testament (7)

DOWN

1. He was stoned to death (7) (Acts 7.59)
2. He prayed at midnight (5) (Acts 16.25)
3. Sapphira's husband (7) (Acts 5.1)
5. Bread enough and to . . . . . (5) (Luke 15.17)

VOWELS ONLY

This is a list of books which can be found in the Bible. All the consonants have been left out, leaving only the vowels. Can you complete this list of names?

1. - e - e - i -
2. - u - - e - -
3. - u - -
4. - e - e - i a -
5. - - a - - -
6. - - o - e - - -
7. - a - a - - u -
8. - a - u -
9. - a - a - i a - -
10. - - i - i - - i a - -
11. - o - o - - i a - -
12. - e - - e - -

STRANGERS

Each of these groups contains one stranger who does not belong in that set. Can you pick the stranger from each group?

1. Genesis, Exodus, Numbers, Deuteronomy, Psalms.
2. Abraham, John, Habakkuk, Proverbs, Acts.
3. John, Mark, Timothy, Matthew, Luke.
4. Ruth, Esther, Mary, Samson, Anna.
5. Psalms, Jeremiah, Job, Judges, Romans.

19

CROSSWORD NO. 5

ACROSS

1. The 32nd book of the Old Testament (5)
5. It is not yet (3) (Mark 13.7)
7. The Egyptians are . . . (3) (Isaiah 31.3)
8. It cannot come between them (3) (Job 41.16)
9. A . . . of robbers (3) (Jeremiah 7.11)
11. The 21st book of the New Testament (5)

DOWN

2. The father of Joshua (3) (Joshua 1.1)
3. The brother of John (5) (Mark 1.19)
4. God created it (5) (Genesis 1.1)
5. Opposite of beginning (3) (Revelation 21.6)
6. A son of Jacob (3) (Genesis 30.6)
10. Kill and . . . (3) (Acts 10.13)

CROSSWORD NO. 6

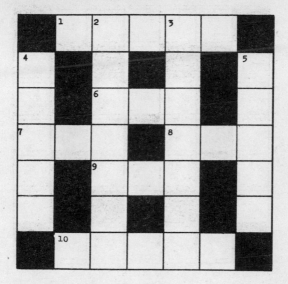

ACROSS

1. A judge of Israel (5) (Judges 12.13)
6. . . . and eat (3) (Isaiah 55.1)
7. What God called the light (3) (Genesis 1.5)
8. What God is not (3) (Numbers 23.19)
9. The lot is cast into it (3) (Proverbs 16.33)
10. . . . . . their teeth (RSV) or . . . . .ing of teeth (AV) (5) (Matthew 8.12)

DOWN

2. Where Nebuchadnezzar was king (7) (Daniel 1.1)
3. St Paul sent greetings to him (7) (Romans 16.15)
4. Where Saul met a medium (5) (1 Samuel 28.7)
5. A high priest (5) (Acts 4.6)

CROSSWORD NO. 7

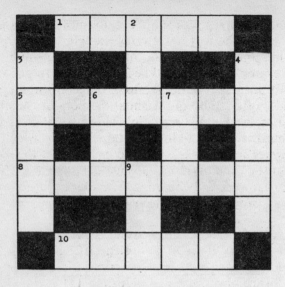

ACROSS

1. Animals (5) (Job 39.1)
5. The first book of the New Testament (7)
8. Simon amazed this nation (7) (Acts 8.9)
10. He fled from Pharaoh (5) (Exodus 2.15)

DOWN

2. Fit, suitable (3) (1 Timothy 3.2)
3. Son of Ithra (5) (2 Samuel 17.25)
4. Every tongue shall . . . . . (5) (Isaiah 45.23)
6. To whom is the 15th book of the New Testament addressed? (abbreviation) (3)
7. The angel departed from . . . (3) (Luke 1.38)
9. Animal (3) (2 Peter 2.16)

FATHERS AND SONS

In Biblical times people did not use surnames, as we do. But one name was not always enough, because people in the same village would often have the same name. For example, there could be 2 or 3 people in one village called Joshua. Therefore, to avoid confusion, people would often talk of 'Joshua the son of Jacob', or 'Joshua the son of Benjamin'. This made it clear which Joshua they were talking about. In Aramaic, which is the language Jesus spoke, the word 'bar' meant 'the son of'. So in the time of Jesus, 'Joshua *bar* Benjamin', meant Joshua *the son of* Benjamin. Now add the father's name to each of the names in the list.

1. Shem bar . . . .   (Genesis 6.10)
2. Isaac bar . . . .   (Genesis 21.3)
3. Joseph bar . . . . .   (Genesis 35.22–24)
4. Joshua bar . . .   (Joshua 1.1)
5. Saul bar . . . .   (1 Samuel 9.3)
6. David bar . . . . .   (1 Samuel 17.17)
7. Solomon bar . . . . .   (1 Kings 1.13)
8. Isaiah bar . . . .   (Isaiah 1.1)
9. Jeremiah bar . . . . (Jeremiah 1.1)
10. James bar . . . . (Mark 1.19)
11. John bar . . . .   (Mark 1.19)
    (The Apostle)
12. John bar . . . . (Luke 1.59–60)
    (The Baptist)

ALPHABET: BIBLICAL PLACES

Complete the alphabet by finding out the names of places which are mentioned in your Bible. You are given the first letter of each name, a short clue and a reference to help you.

A......   Where the disciples were first called
              Christians   (Acts 11.26)
B.....   Where Nebuchadnezzar was king
                                    (2 Kings 25.1)
C........   Where Jesus taught in the synagogue
                                    (Mark 1.21)
D.......   Where Saul was going when he was
              converted   (Acts 9.3)
E.....   A village near Jerusalem
                                    (Luke 24.13)
F.........   A harbour in Crete   (Acts 27.8)
G......   The district around Nazareth
                                    (Luke 4.14)
H.....   Where David was anointed as the King
              of Israel   (2 Samuel 5.3)
I......   St Paul taught in the synagogue at this
              town   (Acts 14.1)
J......   Where the traveller was going in the
              parable of 'The Good Samaritan'
                                    (Luke 10.30)
K.....   A brook   (2 Samuel 15.23)
L.....   St Paul cured a cripple at this town
                                    (Acts 14.8)
M........   St Paul went there because of a vision
                                    (Acts 16.9)
N.......   Jesus lived there   (John 1.45)
O.....   Mount near Jerusalem (Matthew 21.1)

24

P	Leading city of Macedonia (Acts 16.12)
R	An island in the Mediterranean Sea (Acts 21.1)
S	The region between Galilee and Judea (Luke 17.11)
T . . .	A coastal town (Matthew 15.21)
U .	The birthplace of Abraham (Genesis 15.7)
Z . . .	Hill of Jerusalem (1 Kings 8.1)

ANAGRAMS:
PLACES VISITED BY ST PAUL

Anagrams are words with the letters jumbled to make new words; for example, CATS is an anagram of ACTS, and SEAL POST is an anagram of APOSTLES.

The words below are all anagrams of the names of places visited by Saint Paul on his journeys. To begin, see how many you can unscramble without help. Then use your Bible. If it has a map of St Paul's Journeys in the back, that will help, but if not you can look them up in the *Acts of the Apostles*. The chapter and verse is given in brackets after each anagram.

1. SAD MUSCA (9.10)
2. SAIL SAM (13.5)
3. STRAY L (14.8)
4. BREED (14.20)
5. TO CHINA (15.35)
6. ROAST (16.8)
7. HI PIP LIP (16.12)
8. LOAN THIS CASE (17.1)
9. HASTEN (17.15)
10. HIT CORN (18.1)
11. SEE PUSH (18.19)
12. I MELT US (20.17)
13. USE AS CRY (28.12)
14. AS RUST (21.39)
15. MORE (28.16)

25

CROSS-NUMBERS

ACROSS

1. How many tribes of Israel were there? (Genesis 49.28)
3. How many disciples did Jesus choose? (Mark 3.14)
5. How many chapters are there in St Mark's Gospel?
7. How many books are there in the New Testament?
8. How many chapters are there in the book of Job?
10. How many psalms are there in the book of Psalms?
12. How many chapters are there in St Matthew's Gospel?
14. How many chapters are there in the Letter to the Hebrews?
16. How many chapters are there in the book of Hosea?
18. How many chapters are there in Deuteronomy?
20. How many chapters are there in the book of Nehemiah?
22. How many books are contained in the Bible?
23. How many days and nights did Jesus spend in the wilderness? (Luke 4.2)
24. How many books in the Old Testament?
25. 'The Number of the Beast' (Revelation 13.18)
26. Jeremiah foretold .. years of captivity (Jeremiah 25.11)

26

2. How many chapters are there in St Luke's Gospel?
4. How many chapters are there in St John's Gospel?
5. How many plagues were sent upon the Egyptians? (Exodus 7–11)
7. How many chapters are there in the Acts of the Apostles?
9. How many of the books in the New Testament are letters (sometimes called 'epistles')?
11. How many chapters are there in the book of Genesis?
12. How many chapters are there in the book of Joshua?
13. How many chapters are there in St Paul's second letter to the Corinthians?
15. How many chapters are there in the book of Proverbs?
16. How many chapters are there in St Paul's letter to the Romans?
17. How many disciples did Jesus send out on the preaching tour recorded in the tenth chapter of St Luke's Gospel?
19. How many verses in chapter 18 of St Luke's Gospel?
21. How many chapters in the book of Numbers?
22. How many chapters in the book of Isaiah?
23. How many years did the Israelites spend in the wilderness? (Numbers 14.33)

CROSSWORD NO. 8

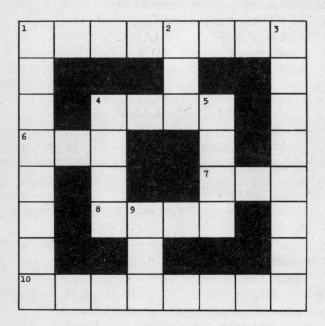

ACROSS

1. The 18th book of the New Testament (8)
4. Be- .... your sin will find you out (4) (Numbers 32.23)
6. Promise (3) (Genesis 28.20)
7. How great is the ... of them (3) (Psalm 139.17)
8. Without him was not anything .... (4) (John 1.3)
10. .... Meshach and Abednego (8) (Daniel 3.14)

1. The 20th book of the Old Testament (8)
2. Incline your . . . (3) (Psalm 45.10)
3. The 16th book of the Old Testament (8)
4. Those who could . . . . (4) (Acts 27.43)
5. Women that are at . . . . (4) (Isaiah 32.9)
9. The first word in Chapter 4 of St Luke's Gospel (3)

MINI-QUIZ: LANGUAGES

1. What was the original language of the Old Testament?
2. What was the original language of the New Testament?
3. What language did Jesus speak?
4. Into what language did Jerome translate the Bible?
5. What was Jerome's translation called?
6. Into what language did King Alfred the Great translate parts of the Bible?
7. What are alpha and omega? (see Revelation 1.8)

MISSING VOWELS

All the vowels (a, e, i, o, u) have been left out of the names of the Biblical books in this list. How many names can you recognize?
1. — Z R —
2. — S T H — R
3. — C C L — S — — S T — S
4. — S — — — H
5. H — S — —
6. — Z — K — — L
7. — M — S
8. — B — D — — H

29

ALPHABET:
PEOPLE IN THE NEW TESTAMENT

Complete the alphabet by finding the names of people whom you can read about in the New Testament. You are given the first letter of each name, a short clue and a Bible reference to help you.

A.....   Brother of Simon
                            (Mark 1.16)

B.......   A murderer   (Mark 15.7)

C........   A Roman Centurion
                            (Acts 10.1)

D........   A silversmith (Acts 19.24)

E........   Mother of John the Baptist
                            (Luke 1.57)

F.....   Sent St Paul to Caesar
                            (Acts 25.12)

G......   An angel   (Luke 1.26)

H....   A ruler of Jerusalem
                            (Matthew 2.3)

I.......   Second name of Judas
                            (Mark 3.19)

K...   Title of the ruler in question (H)
                            (Matthew 2.3)

L......   Jesus raised him from the dead
                            (John 11.43)

M.....   Sister of L above
                            (John 11.39)

N........   A ruler of the Jews
                            (John 3.1)

O.......   'Faithful and beloved brother'
                            (Colossians 4.9)

P....   Denied Jesus (Luke 22.61)

Q	Paul sent his greetings
	(Romans 16.23)
R	Answered Peter's knock
	(Acts 12.13)
S	Chosen to be a deacon
	(Acts 6.5)
T	Paul wrote to him
	(17th New Testament book)
U	'Fellow-worker in Christ'
	(Romans 16.9)
	(AV has one letter less)
Z	A chief tax-collector
	(Luke 19.2)

A BIBLE CODE

Look up these Bible references. Then write down the word specified in the code. For example, Genesis 1.1 (1st word) would give you the word *in*. When you have completed your list you will have a prayer taken from one of the letters of St Paul.

1. Matthew 1.1   (1st word)
2. Ephesians 6.24   (1st word)
3. Luke 7.34   (3rd word)
4. Mark 1.1   (1st word)
5. Luke 2.29   (1st word)
6. Mark 2.19   (2nd word)
7. Galatians 3.13   (1st word)
8. Ephesians 1.3   (2nd word)
9. Ephesians 4.2   (1st word)
10. Luke 10.3   (2nd word)
11. Luke 8.55   (3rd word)

Do you know which letter this verse is from?

HEXAGONS

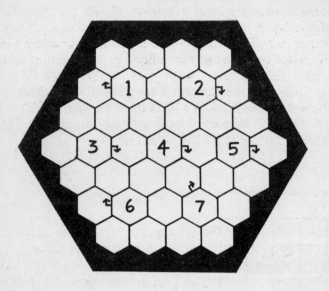

In this puzzle the answers are written clockwise around the number. Start with the hexagon containing the arrow.

1. The Sidonian name for Mount Hermon
                               (Deuteronomy 3.9)
2. The mother of Timothy   (2 Timothy 1.5)
3. A brother of Joseph   (Genesis 37.29)
4. King David reigned here   (2 Samuel 5.1)
5. The sixth book of the Old Testament
6. The language of the Jews   (John 19.20)
7. The seventeenth book of the Old Testament

FIND THE BOOKS

To complete this puzzle you will need to find ten words, each containing four letters, to match the clues. But don't be in too big a hurry to write them in; sometimes you will think of more than one four-letter word to match the clue and the difficult part is deciding which one is the right one.

Column 1 and Column 3 each contain the name of a New Testament book, and as there are not many books in the New Testament with a name of ten letters this should help you to fill in the puzzle.

A cereal

Not closed

God is ****

**** his commandments

Flavouring

A light in the sky

**** thy hands I commit my spirit

Sour

Midday

Israel had twelve

ACROSS

1. Famous for its cedar trees (7) (2 Kings 14.9)
6. Who shall . . . . . in his holy place (5) (Psalm 24.3)
9. An Assyrian insect (3) (Isaiah 7.18)
10. Let it be attentive (3) (Nehemiah 1.6)
11. The . . . . . of one crying in the wilderness (5) (Luke 3.4)
12. To tell an untruth (3) (Acts 5.3)
13. One of the twelve tribes of Israel (3) (Numbers 1.38)
14. Give him whatever he . . . . . (5) (Luke 11.8) (RSV)
17. The ruler of a synagogue (7) (Acts 18.8.)

2. A winged mammal (3) (Deuteronomy 14.18)
3. The father of Joshua (3) (Joshua 1.1)
4. Nebuchadnezzar ruled there (7) (Daniel 1.1)
5. The place where 17 Across was the ruler of the synagogue (7) (Acts 18.1)
6. The number of days for which Joshua besieged Jericho (5) (Joshua 6.15)
7. . . . . . in me (5) (John 15.4)
8. Their . . . . . were evil (5) (John 3.19)
15. The priest at Shiloh (3) (1 Samuel 1.9)
16. . . . your morsel in the wine (or vinegar) (3) (Ruth 2.14)

THE SECRET WAY

I	A	M	U	T	H
E	H	T	R	N	A
W	H	E	T	D	T
A	T	D	L	E	H
Y	A	N	I	F	E

Start with the letter I in the top left-hand corner of the puzzle. You may move to the next space, upwards, downwards, to the right or to the left, but you must not move diagonally. This puzzle is similar to a maze and you have to find the secret way which takes you from the start to the finish, which is the letter E in the bottom right-hand corner.

If you find the right way you will use each letter once only and your journey will spell out a well-known saying of Jesus.

Can you find that saying?

CRAZY COUPLES

In these lists of well-known partners the pairing is mixed-up. See if you can sort out the names, so that each person is with the right partner.

(A) Adam and Delilah, Samson and Jezabel, Ahab and Eve, Ananias and Priscilla, Aquila and Sapphira.

ADAM AND ....   SAMSON AND ....
AHAB AND ....   ANANIAS AND ....
AQUILA AND ....

(B) Cain and Jonathan, Jacob and Aaron, Moses and Naomi, David and Abel, Ruth and John, James and Esau.

CAIN AND................   MOSES AND ....
JACOB AND ....   DAVID AND ....
RUTH AND..............   JAMES AND ....

(C) Abraham and his ass, Moses and the Temple, Joshua and the burning bush, Elijah and the Promised Land, Balaam and the Battle of Jericho, Solomon and the ravens.

ABRAHAM AND ......   MOSES AND ....
JOSHUA AND ....   ELIJAH AND............
BALAAM AND.........   SOLOMON AND ......

RIDDLE

She was a prophetess with a palindromic name. By adding the same letter to the beginning and to the end of her name you will make the name of the mother of Samuel. What is the name of the prophetess and what was the letter that you used to change her name?

NAME-SEARCH

*	P	H	I	L	E	S	S	A	L
A	I	P	P	I	H	T	Y	H	O
N	O	R	N	S	S	I	A	T	N
S	C	I	A	E	E	S	N	O	I
I	T	N	I	P	H	T	I	M	A
A	A	T	H	U	T	I	T	S	N
N	L	A	G	S	S	I	A	E	M
S	M	A	C	O	S	S	N	L	O
R	O	N	S	L	O	P	H	I	N

Starting with the square containing the star at the top left-hand corner of the square, spell out the names of ten people and churches to whom St Paul wrote letters, all of which can be found in the New Testament.

You may move to the next space upwards, downwards or sideways but you must not move diagonally. Every letter is used once only.

In this puzzle the books are *not* in the order in which they appear in the New Testament.

BIBLE CODE

Are you ready to search for another verse written in the Bible code which appears on Page 31?

1. Ephesians 2.8 (3rd word)
2. James 1.22 (2nd word)
3. Ephesians 4.2 (1st word)
4. 1 Corinthians 6.12 (1st word)
5. Luke 7.34 (3rd word)
6. 1 Thessalonians 3.6 (last word)
7. Romans 1.25 (last word)

37

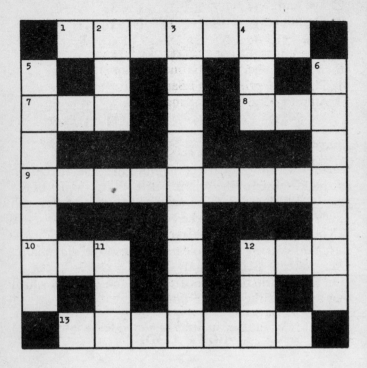

ACROSS

1. Wife of David (7) (1 Samuel 25.42)
7. It means 'the son of' (3)
8. The lot is cast into it (3) (Proverbs 16.33)
9. The 3rd book in the Old Testament (9)
10. The father of Joshua (3) (Joshua 1.1)
12. Everyone (3) (John 1.7)
13. A brother of Joab (7) (2 Samuel 23.18)

2. The same as 7 Across (3)
3. The 9th book of the New Testament (9)
4. Sick, bad (3)
5. Where Lysanias ruled (7) (Luke 3.1)
6. St Paul was called to be one (7) (Romans 1.1)
11. City of the priests (3) (1 Samuel 22.19)
12. A king of Judah (3) (1 Kings 15.9)

RIDDLE-ME-REE

My first is in sun but not in moon;
　My second in hymn but isn't in tune;
My third is in hand and also in span;
　My fourth in woman as well as in man;
My fifth is in dog but not in bear;
　My sixth is in oath but never in swear;
My seventh is number five again;
　My eighth is in downpour but not in rain;
My last is in zero if not in nought;
　My whole is a building in which Jesus taught.

APOSTLES IN HIDING

Can you find the names of the Apostles? There is one name hidden in each of these sentences.
1. 'Just a minute,' Ernie said.
2. Perhaps he is lost in Portugal.
3. Sam is my own name.
4. Mick and Tommy Turner heaved enormous weights.
5. Jim only has nine.

39

CROSSWORD NO. 11

ACROSS

 1. A son of Etam (7) (1 Chronicles 4.3)
 5. They thought Peter was one (5) (Acts 12.15)
 7. The 15th book of the Old Testament (4)
 8. The first man (4) (Genesis 3.21)
10. The first Greek letter (5) (Revelation 21.6)
11. She came to welcome Festus (7) (Acts 25.13)

2. Drowsiness clothes in .... (4) (Proverbs 23.21)
3. The first book in the Old Testament (7)
4. A son of Abraham and Hagar (7) (Genesis 16.16)
5. The sea of ..... (5) (Acts 27.27)
6. A seller of purple goods (5) (Acts 16.14)
9. A measurement (4) (Exodus 28.16)

RIDDLE-ME-REE

My first is in country but isn't in land;
    My second in palm as well as in hand;
My third is in seven, eight, nine and ten;
    My fourth is in soldiers but isn't in men;
My fifth is in Roman but never in Jew;
    My last in purple but not in pale blue;
My whole was the ruler of many a land
    With conquering armies at his command.

WHAT DOES IT MEAN?

All of these Aramaic words are to be found in St Mark's
Gospel. The chapters and verses are given in the
brackets. Look them up, and you will find out what they
mean.

1. Talitha cumi   (5.41)
2. Corban   (7.11)
3. Ephphatha   (7.34)
4. Golgotha   (15.22)
5. Eloi, eloi, lama sabachthani (15.34)

NAME-SPIRAL

Start at the arrow and work clockwise around the spiral until you reach the centre. Each answer ends with the first two letters of the next answer, and this overlap will help you to complete the puzzle.

1. Jonah's ship was going there   (Jonah 1.3)
2. A son of Hotham   (1 Chronicles 11.44)
3. The last book of the Old Testament
4. A king of Tyre   (2 Samuel 5.11)
5. Aaron's father-in-law   (Exodus 6.23)
6. A river in Damascus   (2 Kings 5.12)
7. Ruth's mother-in-law   (Ruth 1.22)
8. An Archangel   (Jude, verse 9)
9. A prophet   (1 Kings 18.1)
10. A king of Israel   (1 Kings 18.1)
11. Father of Isaac   (Genesis 21.3)

12. Chief of Absalom's army   (2 Samuel 17.25)
13. God called this boy   (1 Samuel 3.4)
14. Mother of John the Baptist   (Luke 1.57)
15. St Paul taught in this synagogue (Acts 17.1)
16. Where the prophets of Baal gathered
                              (1 Kings 18.20)
17. The son of Shephat   (1 Kings 19.19)
18. The father of Canaan   (Genesis 9.18)
19. Saul cut them down   (1 Samuel 11.11)
20. The seventeenth book of the Old Testament
21. One of St Paul's helpers   (Acts 19.22)

EARNING THEIR LIVINGS

Senior 16/10/88

What were the occupations of the people named in the list below? Answer as many as you can without looking, and then use the Bible references to help you with the others.

1. Annas   (Luke 3.2)
2. Aquila   (Acts 18.2–3)
3. Boaz   (Ruth 2.2–3)
4. Cornelius   (Acts 10.1)
5. Demetrius   (Acts 19.24)
6. Esau   (Genesis 25.27)
7. Felix   (Acts 23.24)
8. Luke   (Colossians 4.14)
9. Lydia   (Acts 16.14)
10. Naaman   (2 Kings 5.1)
11. Onesimus   (Philemon vs. 15–16)
12. Paul   (Acts 18.2–3)

HEXAGONS

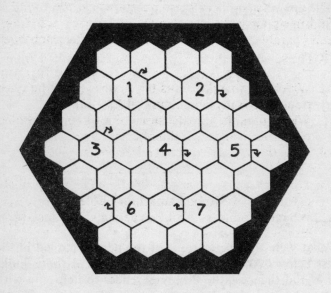

In this puzzle the answers are written clockwise around the number. Start with the hexagon which contains the arrow.

1. Wrongdoer   (Luke 15.7)
2. A king of Judah   (2 Kings 22.1)
3. A Syrian leper   (Luke 4.27)
4. People of Rome   (John 11.48)
5. Lend but do not . . . . . .   (Deuteronomy 15.6)
6. A man of great strength   (Judges 16.30)
7. . . . . . . in my heart   (Psalm 13.2)

MINI-QUIZ: PARABLES

Jesus told many parables. How well do you know them?
The answers to all of these questions can be found in
St Luke's Gospel. The chapter and verses containing
each parable are given in the brackets after each question.

1. Which parable did Jesus tell in answer to the question 'Who is my neighbour?' (10.25–37)
2. Which parable tells the story of a father, a reckless
   younger son and his jealous older brother? (15.11–32)
3. Jesus told a parable about a tree which gave no fruit.
   What kind of tree was it? (13.6–9)
4. Towards which town was the traveller going in the
   parable of The Good Samaritan? (10.25–27)
5. Which parable is about a person who lost some
   money? (15.8–10)
6. Which parable concerns a lost animal? (15.3–7)
7. What was the name of the beggar in the parable
   about a rich man and a beggar? (16.19–31)
8. Which parable gave some good advice about building a house? (6.46–49)
9. Which parable is about a man who scattered seeds?
   (8.5–8)
10. Which parable is about a tiny seed which becomes
    something great? (13.18–19)
11. What character in a parable prayed in these words
    'God be merciful to me, a sinner'? (18.10–14)
12. Which parable is about making bread? (13.20–21)

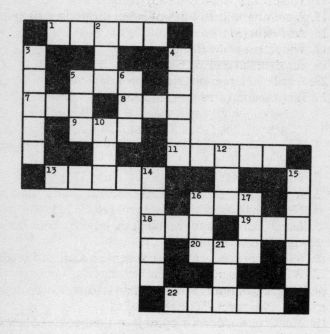

1. The 17th book of the New Testament (5)
5. Not many (3) (Luke 10.2)
7. A king of Judah (3) (1 Kings 15.9)
8. No room there (3) (Luke 2.7)
9. The number of chapters in the book of Esther (3)
11. The brother of Andrew (5) (Mark 1.16)
13. A country to the North of Israel (5) (Judges 10.6)
16. An insect (3)
18. The father of Joshua (3) (Joshua 1.1)
19. . . . drink and be merry (3) (Luke 12.19)
20. A tribe of Israel (3) (Numbers 1.38)
22. Instruments of . . . . . (5) (1 Samuel 18.6)*

2. The first word in the New Testament (3)
3. A son of Abraham (5) (Genesis 21.3)
4. The 11th book of the Old Testament (5)
5. The . . . of the land (3) (Genesis 45.18)
6. Gain (3) (2 Chronicles 32.1)
10. The organ of hearing (3) (Nehemiah 1.6)
12. What God is not (3) (Numbers 23.19)
14. A cousin of Saul (5) (1 Samuel 14.50)
15. . . . . . his gates (5) (Psalm 100.4)
16. The first word in Chapter 9 of the book of Genesis (3)
17. The same as 9 Across (3)
21. The bridle is for this animal (3) (Proverbs 26.3)

  * Usual spelling, not as in AV.

1. An animal (3) (Genesis 15.9)
3. A tool for cutting (3) (Luke 3.9)
4. The . . . of the Covenant (3) (1 Samuel 4.5)
6. Meet the Lord in the . . . (3) (1 Thessalonians 4.17)
7. Boat (4) (Acts 27.2)
9. Faults (4) (1 John 1.9)
12. Not one (4) (Psalm 14.1)
15. . . . . for . . . . (4) (Job 2.4)
17. St Paul cut his hair because he had a . . . (3) (Acts 18.18)
18. . . . witnesses (3) (Luke 1.2)
19. A king of Judah (3) (1 Kings 15.9)
20. They shall . . . and not be weary (3) (Isaiah 40.31)

DOWN

1. Harvest the crops (4) (Galatians 6.7)
2. A planet named after the Roman god of war (4)
3. A type of tree (3)
5. The next of . . . (. . . sman in AV) (3) (Ruth 4.1)
7. A boy child (3) (1 Samuel 1.23)
8. A place for travellers (3) (Luke 2.7)
10. Writing fluid (3) (2 Corinthians 3.3)
11. God is a . . . and shield (3) (Psalm 84.11)
13. How many chapters are there in St Paul's Letter to Philemon? (3)
14. The word of God shall stand for . . . . (4) (Isaiah 40.8)
15. A water bird (4)
16. A Jairite (3) (2 Samuel 20.26)

INThabaGINUIUG9O

PCHeeTadLhahaa

NeuSenPTYeaaRTY

This message is a very well-known verse from the Bible.
It isn't written in Greek or in any other foreign language.
In fact, it is quite easy to read it when you have worked
out the secret.

What do you notice about the shapes of *all* of the
letters? Now look at the letters one at a time and see if
any shapes look familiar. By now you should be exactly
half-way to finding the message.

Do you know *exactly* where in the Bible this verse can
be found?

THE SECRET WAY 2

A	N	E	W	M	M	D	M	T	I
A	H	T	C	O	A	N	E	N	G
T	Y	U	O	Y	O	T	E	V	I
U	O	E	O	N	E	A	N	H	E
L	O	V	H	I	S	A	O	T	R
L	E	V	A	L	S	N	E	V	E
O	V	E	D	A	O	O	N	T	H
T	U	O	Y	U	L	E	E	O	E
H	A	T	Y	O	O	V	A	N	R

Start with the letter A in the top left-hand corner of the puzzle. You may move to the next space, upwards, downwards, to the right or to the left, but you must not move diagonally.

If you find the secret way through this puzzle you will use each letter once only and finish with the R in the bottom right-hand corner. Again, your journey will spell out a well-known saying of Jesus.

Can you find that saying?

MINI-QUIZ: THE TWELVE APOSTLES

The answers to all these questions can be found in Mark 3.16–19.
1. Who was the father of James and John?
2. Which disciple was known as the Canaanean (or Canaanite)?
3. To which disciple did Jesus give the name of Peter?
4. To which two disciples did Jesus give the nickname Boanerges or Sons of Thunder?
5. Which of the disciples betrayed Jesus?

51

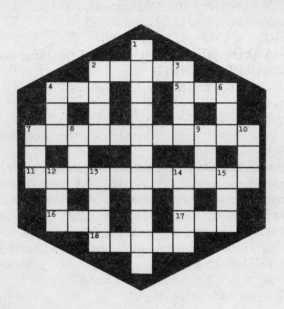

ACROSS

2. The Queen of . . . . . visited King Solomon (5) (1 Kings 10.1)
4. The lot is cast into it (3) (Proverbs 16.33)
5. The name of an idol (3) (Jeremiah 50.2)
7. Bearers of good tidings (11) (Ephesians 4.11)
11. Nahor was in this land (11) (Genesis 24.10)
16. The wife of Adam (3) (Genesis 3.20)
17. A place in the eastern boundary of Canaan (3) (Numbers 34.11)
18. The name of a high place (5) (Ezekiel 20.29)

1. The 5th book of the Old Testament (11)
2. A measurement (4) (Isaiah 40.12)
3. A son of Elam (4) (Ezra 10.26)
4. An abbreviation for the name of the third book in the Old Testament (3)
6. Saved from destruction (3) (Genesis 19.29)
7. A tree (3)
8. An animal (3) (Matthew 21.5)
9. An abbreviation for the name of the ninth book in the Old Testament (3)
10. Jesus met Simon and Andrew when they were casting a net into it (3) (Mark 1.16)
12. The same as 16 Across (3)
13. A Midianite prince (4) (Judges 7.25)
14. The wife of Esau (4) (Genesis 36.2)
15. The Good Samaritan took the injured traveller to one (3) (Luke 10.34)

MORE ANAGRAMS

All these anagrams are the jumbled names of books of the Old and New Testaments. How many can you unscramble?

1. RAZE
2. THREES
3. LEAD IN
4. NOR SAM
5. SUIT CLIVE
6. LAME US
7. MELAN STATION
8. A SHOE
9. MET WHAT
10. HER WEBS

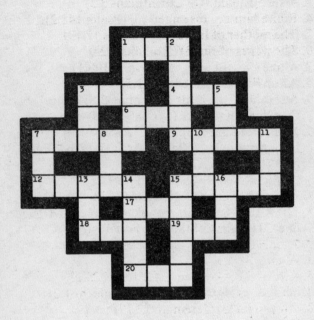

ACROSS

1. The 18th book of the Old Testament (3)
3. The . . . of peace (3) (Luke 10.6)
4. Writing fluid (3) (2 Corinthians 3.3)
6. Praise him . . . his angels (3) (Psalm 148.2)
7. The mother of Isaac (5) (Genesis 17.19)
9. The wages of sin (5) (Romans 6.23)
12. Make a joyful . . . . . (5) (Psalm 100.1)
15. At no time (5) (Hebrews 13.5)
17. Stand in . . . of him (3) (Psalm 33.8)
18. The birds of the . . . (3) (Luke 9.58)
19. Plant (3) (Luke 8.5)
20. . . . glory covered the heavens (3) (Habakkuk 3.3)

DOWN

1. The 32nd book of the Old Testament (5)
2. A time to . . . . . up (5) (Ecclesiastes 3.3)
3. A gate (3) (2 Kings 11.6)
5. Ally of the Assyrians (3) (Ezekiel 23.23)
7. The . . . of righteousness (3) (Malachi 4.2)
8. An animal (3) (Jeremiah 22.19)
10. The mother of all living (3) (Genesis 3.20)
11. A companion of Moses (3) (Exodus 17.10)
13. A Jairite (3) (2 Samuel 20.26)
14. It shall be burned up (5) (2 Peter 3.10)
15. Birds have them (5) (Luke 9.58)
16. Promise (3) (Judges 11.39)

```
*   I   T   A   O   N   Z   E
A   S   N   T   I   S   E   K
I   M   E   A   D   L   E   I
A   A   L   N   O   S   E   A
H   A   H   I   H   E   O   J
J   I   M   E   L   L   A   M
E   R   E           H   A   O
H   A   C           J   I   S
N   A   I           O   D   O
U   H   M   H   A   N   A   B
M   I   A   A   G   G   H   B
H   N   H   H   I   A   A   M
A   A   H   P   Z   R   I   A
B   K   U   E   E   A   C   L
A   K   K   Z   C   H   H   I
```

Starting with the square containing the star at the top left-hand corner of the puzzle, spell out the names of seventeen books of the Bible.

You may move to the next space upwards, downwards or sideways but not diagonally. Every letter is used once only.

The books are in the order in which they are found in the Bible, and all have something in common. Make a list of the books. What have they in common?

HEXAGONS

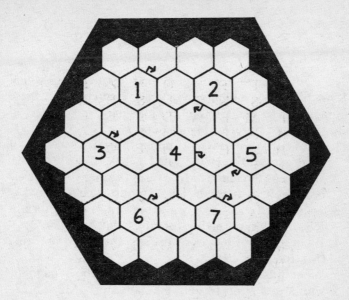

In this puzzle the answers are written clockwise around the number. Start with the hexagon which contains the arrow.

1. Place in the land of the tribe of Issachar
(Joshua 19.18)
2. The Rose of . . . . . . (Song of Solomon 2.1)
3. Opposite of wide (Matthew 7.14)
4. A village near Jerusalem (Luke 24.13)
5. Where Jacob met God 'face to face'
(Genesis 32.30)
6. A parent (Ezekiel 16.44)
7. An Egyptian city built by the Israelites
(Exodus 1.11)

MINI-QUIZ: MIRACLES

The Four Gospels tell of many marvellous things which Jesus did. How much can you remember about these miracles? The Bible references are given in brackets in case you need to refresh your memory.

1. Jesus cured the fever of the mother-in-law of one of his disciples. Which disciple? (Mark 1.29–31)
2. What was the name of Martha's brother whom Jesus brought back from the dead? (John 11.38–44)
3. Jesus cured the illness of the servant of an important Roman. What was the Roman? (Matthew 8.5–13)
4. What kind of illness was the servant suffering from? (Matthew 8.5–13)
5. What was the name of the ruler of the synagogue who asked Jesus to cure his daughter? (Mark 5.22–24 and 35–43)
6. How old was the daughter? (Mark 5.42)
7. Jesus changed water into wine at a wedding-feast. In what town did this happen? (John 2.1–11)
8. He healed a man whom Peter had injured with a sword. What was that man? (Luke 22.50–51)
9. On which day did Jesus heal a man who had a withered hand? (Mark 3.1–5)
10. To what did Jesus say 'Peace, be still'? (Mark 4.35–41)

CROSSWORD NO. 16

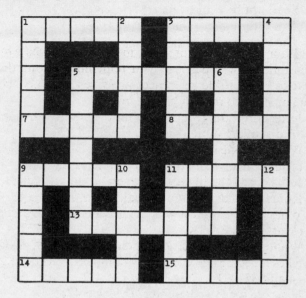

ACROSS

1. The . . . . . of death is sin (5) (1 Corinthians 15.56)
3. When man's eyes are satisfied (5) (Proverbs 27.20)
5. The first book of the New Testament (7)
7. The scribes wanted the best (5) (Mark 12.38–39)
8. To appear three times a year (5) (Exodus 23.17)
9. The shape of the molten sea (5) (1 Kings 7.23)
11. The hornet shall . . . . . them out (5) (Exodus 23.28)
13. The end of the day (7) (Mark 14.17)
14. Twelve in a day? (5) (John 11.9)
15. The 11th book of the Old Testament (5)

1. Can the leopard change them? (5) (Jeremiah 13.23)
2. Shall not be shut by day (5) (Revelation 21.25)
3. The 34th book of the Old Testament (5)
4. The lowest part of the fig-tree (5) (Mark 11.20)
5. The . . . . of faith (7) (Romans 12.3)
6. The men looked like trees . . . . (7) (Mark 8.24)
9. The opposite of smooth (5) (Luke 3.5)
10. The last drops (5) (Psalm 75.8)
11. David would not do this (5) (2 Samuel 23.16)
12. They have committed two (5) (Jeremiah 2.13)

RIDDLE-ME-REE

My first is in order but isn't in law;
   My second in fear and also in awe;
My third is in under but not in below;
   My fourth in grant and also bestow;
My fifth is in error and in mistake;
   My sixth in batter, fracture and break;
My seventh in honour as well as obey;
   My eighth is in no and also in nay;
My ninth is the same as number seven;
   My tenth is in moon but not found in heaven;
My last is in hay but isn't in straw;
   My whole? An Old Testament book of the Law.

CROSSWORD NO. 17

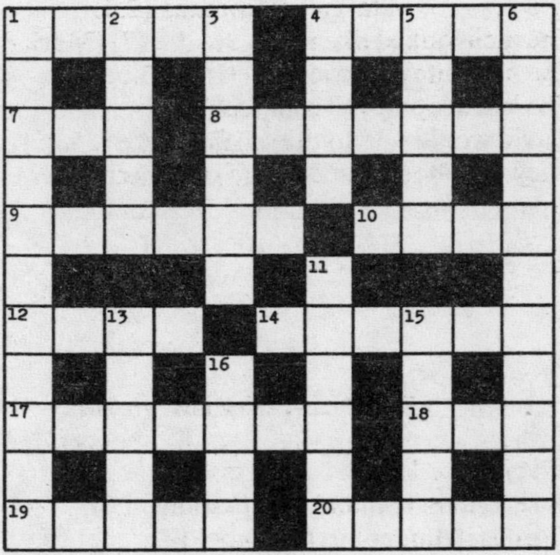

1. A High Priest (5) (Luke 3.2)
4. Facial hair (5) (Psalm 133.2)
7. Writing fluid (3) (Jeremiah 36.18)
8. 122 men (7) (Ezra 2.27)
9. To serve . . . . . . (6) (Acts 6.2)
10. Over against Egypt (4) (1 Samuel 15.7)
12. A Canaanite god (4) (1 Kings 16.32)
14. Ten cubits high (6) (1 Kings 6.25)
17. The cedars of . . . . (7) (1 Kings 5.6)
18. Abraham's nephew (3) (Genesis 11.31)
19. St Paul's chosen companion (5) (Acts 15.40)
20. Son of Ezrah (5) (1 Chronicles 4.17)

DOWN

1. A Roman Christian (11) (Romans 16.10)
2. Border towns: Adami . . . . . and Jabneel (5) (Joshua 19.33)
3. The ninth book of the Old Testament (6)
4. He turned his . . . . to leave (4) (1 Samuel 10.9)
5. A city of the plain (5) (Hosea 11.8)
6. Gave out (11) (John 6.11)
11. The Philistines camped here (6) (1 Samuel 28.4)
13. Beth . . . . . was a fortress (5) (Hosea 10.14)
15. A person who rules (5) (Proverbs 6.7)
16. Insects (4) (Proverbs 30.25)

CROSSWORD NO. 18

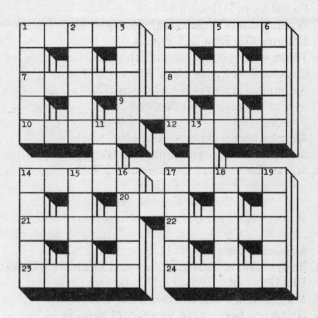

ACROSS

1. The city of a famous tower (5) (Genesis 11.9)
4. Son of Abraham (5) (Genesis 22.2)
7. The language of the Romans (5) (John 19.20)
8. A son of Jesse (5) (1 Samuel 17.17)
9. A gatekeeper (3) (Ezra 10.24)
10. Wine is not for . . . . . (5) (Proverbs 31.4)
12. Joab killed him (5) (2 Samuel 3.27)
14. Sacred songs (5) (Colossians 3.16)

17. A trap (5) (Amos 3.5)
20. A priest (3) (1 Samuel 1.9)
21. St Paul intended to visit this country (5) (Romans 15.24)
22. A grandson of Noah (5) (Genesis 10.2)
23. 8th son of Jacob (5) (Genesis 30.13)
24. These were more . . . . . (5) (Acts 17.11)

DOWN

 1. King of Moab (5) (Joshua 24.9)
 2. A border town (5) (Joshua 19.25)
 3. A friend of St Paul (5) (2 Timothy 4.21)
 4. An Eastern land (5) (Esther 1.1)
 5. A son of Shobal (5) (Genesis 36.23)
 6. Wood from Lebanon (5) (1 Kings 5.6)
11. Abbreviation for the name of the first book of the Old Testament (3)
13. They called his name . . .-ammi (3) (Genesis 19.38)
14. The 28th book of the Old Testament (5)
15. An ancestor of Jesus (5) (Luke 3.26)
16. A mountain of fir trees (5) (Ezekiel 27.5)
17. Jesus called him Peter (5) (Matthew 4.18)
18. Kingdom of Og (5) (Deuteronomy 3.4)
19. A bird of prey (5) (Job 9.26)

STRANGERS

Each of these groups contains one 'stranger' who does not belong in the set. How many of these strangers can you detect?

1. Eagle, Scorpion, Sparrow, Quail, Raven.
2. Olive, Fig, Frankincense, Pomegranate, Locust.
3. Romans, Syrians, Hebrews, Galatians, Ephesians.
4. Athens, Jerusalem, Philippi, Neapolis, Corinth.
5. Amos, Hosea, Isaac, Isaiah, Jeremiah.
6. Mark, John, Matthew, Paul, Luke.
7. The Good Samaritan, The Widow's Mite, The Sower, The Dishonest Steward, The Prodigal Son.
8. Philistines, Midianites, Syrians, Babylonians, Nazarites, Edomites.
9. Damascus, Jerusalem, Bethany, Bethlehem, Jericho.
10. Benjamin, Joel, Simeon, Reuben, Dan.
11. Jordan, Sinai, Carmel, Horeb, Zion.
12. Promised Land, Canaan, Egypt, Holy Land, Israel.
13. Finger, centimetre, span, handbreadth, cubit.
14. Barabbas, Peter, Andrew, Bartholomew, James.
15. Titus, Daniel, Ruth, Samuel, Esther.
16. Saul, David, Jonathan, Solomon.
17. Judges, Kings, Chronicles, Colossians, Proverbs.
18. Luke, Timothy, Silas, Stephen, Barnabas.

CROSSWORD NO. 19

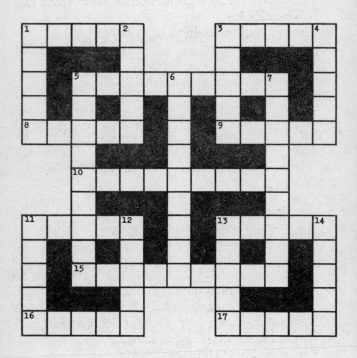

1. A . . . . . of David (5) (Psalm 23)
3. . . . . . years of famine (5) (Genesis 41.36)
5. Supporters of King Herod (9) (Matthew 22.16)
8. Where Jehoiakim's grandmother came from (5) (2 Kings 23.36)
9. The . . . . . of wickedness (5) (Psalm 84.10)
10. And you yourselves . . . . (6, 3) (Luke 13.28)
11. Hard stone (5) (Isaiah 5.28)
13. A victim of Joab (5) (2 Samuel 20.10)
15. Seriously (9) (1 Corinthians 12.31)
16. Her name shall be . . . . . (5) (Genesis 17.15)
17. He shall . . . . . for ever and ever (5) (Revelation 11.15)

1. His name means 'a rock' (5) (Matthew 16.18)
2. A spice (5) (Exodus 30.23)
3. Stem (5) (Exodus 25.31)
4. There were a few, even in Sardis (5) (Revelation 3.4)
5. A descendant of Hamath (9) (Genesis 10.18)
6. To a . . . ., arise! (4, 5) (Habakkuk 2.19)
7. A minister in the . . . . (9) (Hebrews 8.2)
11. Plague insects (5) (Exodus 8.24)
12. Son of Nahor (5) (Genesis 11.24)
13. A place for a sacrifice (5) (Genesis 22.9)
14. A son of David (5) (2 Samuel 3.2)

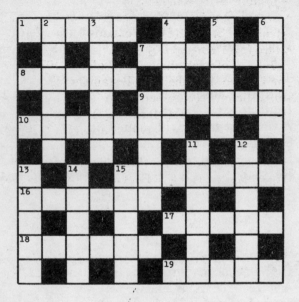

ACROSS

1. The father of Abraham (5) (Luke 3.34)
7. The elders of the Sanhedrin (6) (Acts 5.21)
8. Mountain of the Law (5) (Exodus 19.18)
9. A sum of money (6) (Matthew 25.24)
10. A woman of Athens (7) (Acts 17.34)
15. She ministered to Jesus (7) (Luke 8.3)
16. A church of Asia (6) (Revelation 3.1)
17. Peace (5) (Hebrews 7.2)
18. Leader of a flock (6) (Ephesians 4.11)
19. Son of Ithra (5) (2 Samuel 17.25)

2. A Tishbite (6) (1 Kings 17.1)
3. A high mountain (6) (Genesis 8.4)
4. A friend of St Paul (5) (Colossians 4.14)
5. A bird (5) (1 Kings 17.6)
6. The . . . . . of wickedness (5) (Psalm 84.10)
9. The 17th book of the New Testament (5)
11. Son of Beor (6) (Numbers 22.5)
12. Heavenly beings (6) (Mark 12.25)
13. He wrote hymns for David's choir (5) (2 Chronicles 29.30)
14. . . . . . from the dead (5) (Ephesians 5.14)
15. Where Julius treated St Paul kindly (5) (Acts 27.3)

Senior?
18/8/88   **ANAGRAMS AGAIN**

Here are some more anagrams for you to unscramble. These are more difficult because you have not been given a Bible reference to help you. But there is a useful clue for each one and, of course, every one of these names is to be found in the Bible.

1. BONE   A mountain
2. BONY BAL   Nebuchadnezzar's kingdom
3. CATS   A New Testament book
4. CLOUTS   A plague insect
5. DREAD   A poisonous snake

69

6. ELMO	A burrowing animal
7. EZEEBED	Father of two apostles
8. HILLADE	A Philistine woman
9. HOT SAM	An apostle
10. HURT	An Old Testament book
11. LEAD IN	An Old Testament book
12. LEMON HIP	A New Testament book
13. LINE	A river
14. NAILS	A small slow creature
15. NEED	The first garden
16. NESH PET	The first Christian martyr
17. NEVERTOLIA	A New Testament book
18. RAW NED	An apostle
19. RAZE	An Old Testament book
20. SHAM SEAN	Son of Joseph
21. SHEILA	A prophet
22. SHORE	A useful animal
23. SLAMPS	An Old Testament book
24. SOMA	A prophet and Old Testament book
25. SUE SIMON	A slave
26. TOGA	An animal

Now pick some other words and names from your Bible and try shuffling the letters to make some amusing anagrams of your own.

MINI-QUIZ: BROTHERS

Who was the brother of

CAIN?	(Genesis 4.2)
JACOB?	(Genesis 27.6)
AARON?	(Exodus 4.14)
SIMON PETER?	(Mark 1.16)
JOHN?	(Mark 1.19)

BIBLE CODE 2

Look up these references and write down the words. The list of words will give you a quotation from one of the New Testament letters.

1. Ephesians 6.23	(1st word)
2. Colossians 1.2	(1st word)
3. John 6.37	(1st word)
4. Philippians 4.23	(3rd word)
5. 1 Thessalonians 3.6	(last word)
6. 1 Thessalonians 4.6	(1st word)
7. Matthew 5.3	(2nd word)
8. Colossians 3.7	(1st word)
9. Galatians 3.13	(1st word)

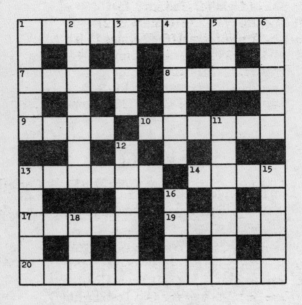

ACROSS

1. The seventh book of the New Testament (11)
7. Young sheep (5) (Isaiah 40.11)
8. Sound (5) (Psalm 100.1)
9. Son of Gera (4) (Judges 3.15)
10. The still . . . . . . (6) (Psalm 23.2)
13. Last king of Israel (6) (2 Kings 15.30)
14. Make well (4) (Deuteronomy 32.39)
17. Protection (5) (Psalm 121.5)
19. Constellation of stars (5) (Job 9.9)
20. St Paul saluted his family (11) (Romans 16.10)

DOWN

1. A female Christian of Corinth (5) (1 Corinthians 1.11)
2. Be not troubled by . . . . of wars (7) (Mark 13.7)
3. I shall die in my . . . . (4) (Job 29.18)
4. Samuel's mother (6) (1 Samuel 1.20)
5. Son of Abdiel (3) (1 Chronicles 5.15)
6. Follow his . . . . . (5) (1 Peter 2.21)
11. The 26th book of the Old Testament (7)
12. I . . . . . . you (6) (Hosea 4.6)
13. The 28th book of the Old Testament (5)
15. They have fallen (5) (Psalm 16.6)
16. David's nephew and the captain of his army (4) (2 Samuel 8.16)
18. The sons of . . . (3) (Ezra 2.57)

CROSSWORD NO. 22

Senior's
30/4/89

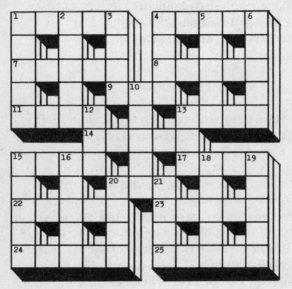

ACROSS

1. This king died in a fire (5) (1 Kings 16.18)
4. Where Melchizedek was king (5) (Genesis 14.18)
7. A great city (5) (Genesis 10.12)
8. David sent ten young men to him (5) (1 Samuel 25.5)
9. The first word in Genesis 1.6 (3)
11. Where a wise man has his eyes (4) (Ecclesiastes 2.14)
13. A son of Zerah (4) (1 Chronicles 2.6)
14. . . . . . zedek was king of Jerusalem (5) (Joshua 10.1)
15. He killed his brother (4) (1 John 3.12)

17. A famous garden (4) (Genesis 2.8)
20. A Gadite (3) (1 Chronicles 5.13)
22. Goliath's brother (5) (1 Chronicles 20.5)
23. The second son of Japheth (5) (Genesis 10.2)
24. The land of Naaman (5) (2 Kings 5.1)
25. Fir trees grew here (5) (Ezekiel 27.5)

DOWN

 1. A town of the tribe of Dan (5) (Joshua 19.41)
 2. A son of Ishmael (5) (Genesis 25.14)
 3. A son of Helem (4) (1 Chronicles 7.35)
 4. This is weighty (4) (Proverbs 27.3)
 5. Part of North Africa (5) (Acts 2.10)
 6. The son of Menna or Menan (5) (Luke 3.31)
10. The mother-in-law of Ruth (5) (Ruth 1.22)
12. One of the twelve tribes of Israel (3) (Numbers 1.38)
13. To . . . is gain (3) (Philippians 1.21)
15. Young horses (5)
16. A son of David (5) (2 Samuel 5.15)
18. A Philistine god (5) (Judges 16.23)
19. Simeon was called by this name (5) (Acts 13.1)
20. A son of Rehoboam (4) (2 Chronicles 11.20)
21. A prophet, and the 30th book of the Old Testament (4)

ANAGRAMS: PEOPLE PAUL KNEW

More anagrams! This time you must re-arrange the letters of these jumbled words to find the names of people known to St Paul. To help you each one has been given a clue about the person. In case you need more help, the brackets after the clue contain the chapter and verse in the Acts of the Apostles or one of St Paul's letters in which you can find a mention of that person. But try to unscramble as many of the anagrams as you can before looking up the references.

1. PET HENS — A deacon and the first Christian martyr (Acts 6.8)

2. A AS IN AN — A disciple at Damascus (Acts 9.10)

3. BAN ARABS — The people of Lystra thought that he was a god (Acts 14.12)

4. ALISS — St Paul chose him for his companion (Acts 15.40)

5. HI MOTTY — St Paul's letters to him became the 15th and 16th books of the New Testament (Acts 16.1)

6. DAILY — She sold purple goods (Acts 16.14)

7. SALPOOL — An eloquent Jew who came from Alexandria (Acts 18.24)

8. SUE STAR — A city treasurer (Romans 16.23)

9. SUTTI — St Paul was unable to find him in Troas (2 Corinthians 2.13)

10. REMUS DIET — A silversmith who lived at Ephesus (Acts 19.24)

FOR THE CODE-BREAKERS

What is the Kingdom of Heaven like? Jesus had many
sayings which answered this question. Here is one of
them, but you will need to de-code it. To give you a
good start the first two letters have been done for you.
Decide how the code works, and then find the answer
that Jesus gave.

JU JT MJLF B HSBJO PG NVTUBSE TFFE XIJDI
IT .. ..
B NBO UPPL BOE TPXFE JO IJT HBSEFO BOE
. ...
JU HSFX BOE CFDBNF B USFF BOE UIF
.. ..
CJSET PG UIF BJS NBEF OFTUT JO JUT
....
CSBODIFT
....

MINI-QUIZ: THE PSALMS

1. How many psalms are to be found in the Book of
   Psalms?
2. Which is the longest of the psalms?
3. How many verses does that psalm contain?
4. You are sure to have heard the psalm which begins
   'The Lord is my shepherd'. Which number is it?
5. What does the word PSALM mean?
6. Which is the shortest of the psalms?
7. In which language were the psalms first written?
8. An English king translated the Book of Psalms from
   Latin into Anglo-Saxon. What was his name?

CROSSWORD NO. 23

ACROSS

1. Younger son of Isaac (5) (Genesis 25.26)
4. Wife of Elimelech (5) (Ruth 1.2)
7. Son of Nahshon (5) (1 Chronicles 2.11)
8. Oriental country (5) (Esther 1.1)
9. A wilderness (3) (Numbers 13.21)
11. Descendants of Esau (4) (Genesis 36.19)
13. 'I am the . . . . vine' (4) (John 15.1)
14. The hill of . . . . . (5) (2 Samuel 2.24)
15. Wild animal (4) (Isaiah 11.7)
17. Brother of 1 Across (5) (Genesis 25.25)

78

20. It came at midnight (3) (Matthew 25.6)
22. The father of Adina (5) (1 Chronicles 11.42)
23. A place on the border (5) (Joshua 19.33)
24. A fruit (5) (Numbers 11.5)
25. Those in need (5) (Psalm 74.21)

DOWN

1. The father of David (5) (Ruth 4.22)
2. Like Carchemish (5) (Isaiah 10.9)
3. The father of Obed (4) (1 Chronicles 2.12)
4. A Galilean city (4) (Luke 7.11)
5. Decently and in . . . . . (5) (1 Corinthians 14.40)
6. The Second Commandment forbids making one (5) (Exodus 20.4)
10. A place in Babylonia (5) (Ezra 2.59)
12. Find the animal which Abraham sacrificed – and then spell it backwards (3) (Genesis 22.13)
13. The first word in the New Testament (3)
15. Fire in his . . . . . (5) (Proverbs 6.27)
16. David dwelt here (5) (Isaiah 29.1)
18. Put to . . . . . (5) (Psalm 40.14)
19. Oneness (5) (Ephesians 4.13)
20. First son of Adam (4) (Genesis 4.1)
21. A thread or a story (4)

COGWHEELS

All the answers are words of four letters. Write the first letter in the space arrowed from the clue number, and then add the other three letters in a clockwise direction around the number.

1. The 30th book of the Old Testament
2. A grandson of Lot (Genesis 19.37)
3. 'a keeper of sheep' (Genesis 4.2)
4. A mountain of Moab (Deuteronomy 32.49)
5. The husband of Ruth (Ruth 4.13)
6. Implement (Deuteronomy 27.5)
7. The prophets of this god were put to death by Elijah (1 Kings 18.40)
8. A son of Joktan (Genesis 10.28)
9. A heavenly body (Job 31.26)
10. A piece of timber (Habakkuk 2.11)

11. It guided the wise men   (Matthew 2.2)
12. A prophetess   (Luke 2.36)
13. Began life   (Psalm 87.6)
14. Source   (Job 19.28)
15. Support   (2 Samuel 22.19)
16. The 15th book of the Old Testament
17. A measure of length   (Exodus 28.16)
18. Tattered clothes   (Proverbs 23.21)
19. An animal   (Deuteronomy 12.15)
20. God . . . . me   (Genesis 45.7)
21. Place of the fallen angels   (2 Peter 2.4)
22. They called him Hermes*   (Acts 14.12)
23. A king of the Amalekites   (1 Samuel 15.8)
24. A king of Israel   (1 Kings 16.29)
25. Gasp   (Psalm 119.131)

* Mercurius in AV.

HIDDEN CREATURES

The names of Biblical creatures are hidden in these sentences. For example, 'Debora*h*, are you going?' contains the word *hare*. You will find the names of three creatures hidden in the same way in each of the sentences.
1. The bowling club at the Green will do very well.
2. If Roger will go at once it might do good.
3. Are you as sure as I am that he noticed the sign at the entrance?
4. She came late but I want you to be early.

81

CROSSWORD NO. 24

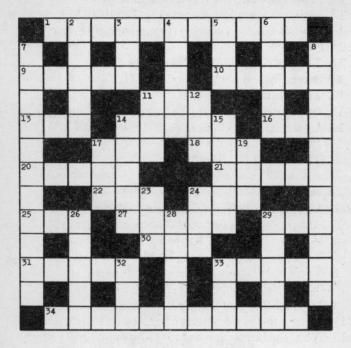

ACROSS

1. The 5th book of the Old Testament (11)
9. The brother of Moses (5) (Exodus 4.14)
10. A son of Resheph (5) (1 Chronicles 7.25)
11. He gave ... only son (3) (John 3.16)
13. The number of chapters in the book of Ezra (3)
14. A son of Jerahmeel (5) (1 Chronicles 2.25)
16. ... things were made by him (3) (John 1.3)
17. They ... in vision (3) (Isaiah 28.7)
18. The opposite of dry (3) (Job 24.8)
20. A type of tree (5) (Revelation 11.4)

21. An animal (5) (Matthew 12.12)
22. Let it be attentive (3) (Nehemiah 1.6)
24. An insect found in Assyria (3) (Isaiah 7.18)
25. Our God is . . . Lord (3) (Deuteronomy 6.4)
27. Eaten (5)
29. A son of Abdiel (3) (1 Chronicles 5.15)
30. Large (3)
31. Sins (5) (Jeremiah 2.13)
33. My joy and . . . . . (5) (Philippians 4.1)
34. A woman from Canaan (11) (1 Chronicles 2.3)

DOWN

2. A Philistine city (5) (1 Samuel 6.16)
3. How many chapters in the book of Esther? (3)
4. A Syrian king (5) (2 Kings 15.37)
5. It is thrown into the sea (3) (Matthew 13.47)
6. A son of Menna (or Menan) (5) (Luke 3.31)
7. One of the Apostles (11) (Acts 1.13)
8. The 11th book of the New Testament (11)
11. Went uphill with Moses (3) (Exodus 17.10)
12. What the blind man did (3) (Matthew 12.22)
14. Jesus took this (5) (Luke 22.19)
15. The son of . . . . . owned all the land of Hepher (5) (1 Kings 4.10)
17. The wife of Adam (3) (Genesis 3.20)
19. The first word in the New Testament (3)
23. A bone (3) (Genesis 2.22)
24. Ask for charity (3) (Luke 16.3)
26. A Harodite (5) (2 Samuel 23.25)
28. A Hebrew month (5) (Nehemiah 2.1)
29. Mixed with myrrh (5) (John 19.39)
32. It was no more (3) (Revelation 21.1)
33. They . . . themselves (3) (1 Kings 18.28)

ANSWERS

The Maze (page 9)

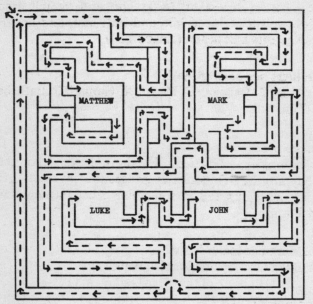

Is it genuine? (page 10)
(i) The Romans didn't reckon their time in years B.C. which means Before Christ. (ii) The Romans used their own system of numerals; 6 would have been written as VI.

Crossword No. 1 (page 11)
Across: 1. James 5. Abraham 6. drink
Down: 2. Malachi 3. Spain 4. Simon

Crossword No. 2 (page 12)
Across: 1. Esther 5. Nahum 7. darts 8. Samuel
Down: 2. Senir 3. Romans 4. Exodus 6. haste

A strange story (page 13)
The passage is written backwards (right to left) as the Hebrew language is written. It reads, 'A man was going down from Jerusalem to Jericho and he fell among robbers who stripped him and beat him, and departed leaving him half dead'. (Luke 10.30)

Mothers and sons (page 13)
1. Sarah 2. Rebekah 3. Rachel 4. Hannah 5. Bathsheba 6. Elizabeth

Name-search (page 14)
Deuteronomy, Leviticus, Exodus, Genesis, Numbers. They are the five books by Moses (not in order); they contain the Law and are sometimes called the Pentateuch or Torah.

Palindromes (page 14)
Hannah, Asa, Nun, Gog, Iri, Anna.

The wheel (page 15)
'And in that region there were shepherds out in the field keeping watch over their flock by night.' (Luke 2.8 – RSV)

Crossword No. 3 (page 16)
Across: 1. palms 5. Troas 7. Hosea 8. truth
Down: 2. Moses 3. Italy 4. Micah 6. Ophir

Alphabet (page 17)
Abraham, Benjamin, Cain, David, Elisha, Gideon, Hannah, Isaac, Jacob, Kish, Lot, Moses, Noah, Omri, Pekah, Reuben, Samson, Tobiah, Uriah, Zadok.

Crossword No. 4 (page 18)
Across: 1. Susanna 4. Lasea 6. Hosea 7. Numbers
Down: 1. Stephen 2. Silas 3. Ananias 5. spare

Vowels only (page 19)
1. Genesis 2. Numbers 3. Ruth 4. Nehemiah 5. Psalms
6. Proverbs 7. Habakkuk 8. Nahum 9. Galatians
10. Philippians 11. Colossians 12. Hebrews

Strangers (page 19)
The set to which the rest of the group belong is mentioned in the brackets following the name of the 'stranger'.
1. Psalms (Books of the Law, or of Moses) 2. Abraham (Biblical books) 3. Timothy (Gospels) 4. Samson (women) 5. Romans (Old Testament books)

Crossword No. 5 (page 20)
Across: 1. Jonah 5. end 7. men 8. air 9. den 11. Peter
Down: 2. Nun 3. James 4. earth 5. end 6. Dan 10. eat

Crossword No. 6 (page 21)
Across: 1. Abdon 6. buy 7. day 8. man 9. lap 10. gnash
Down: 2. Babylon 3. Olympas 4. Endor 5. Annas

Crossword No. 7 (page 22)
Across: 1. goats 5. Matthew 8. Samaria 10. Moses
Down: 2. apt 3. Amasa 4. swear 6. Tim 7. her 9. ass

Fathers and sons (page 23)
1. Noah 2. Abraham 3. Jacob (Israel) 4. Nun 5. Kish
6. Jesse 7. David 8. Amoz 9. Hilkiah 10. Zebedee
11. Zebedee 12. Zechariah (Zacharias)

Alphabet (pages 24–25)
Antioch, Babylon, Capernaum, Damascus, Emmaus, Fair Havens, Galilee, Hebron, Iconium, Jericho, Kidron, Lystra, Macedonia, Nazareth, Olives, Philippi, Rhodes, Samaria, Tyre, Ur, Zion.

Anagrams (page 25)
1. Damascus 2. Salamis 3. Lystra 4. Derbe 5. Antioch 6. Troas 7. Philippi 8. Thessalonica 9. Athens 10. Corinth 11. Ephesus 12. Miletus 13. Syracuse 14. Tarsus 15. Rome.

Cross-numbers (pages 26–27)
Across: 1. 12 3. 12 5. 16 7. 27 8. 42 10. 150 12. 28 14. 13 16. 14 18. 34 20. 13 22. 66 23. 40 24. 39 25. 666 26. 70
Down: 2. 24 4. 21 5. 10 7. 28 9. 21 11. 50 12. 24 13. 13 15. 31 16. 16 17. 70 19. 43 21. 36 22. 66 23. 40

Crossword No. 8 (page 28–29)
Across: 1. Philemon 4. sure 6. vow 7. sum 8. made 10. Shadrach
Down: 1. Proverbs 2. ear 3. Nehemiah 4. swim 5. ease 9. and

Mini-quiz, languages (page 29)
1. Hebrew 2. Greek 3. Aramaic 4. Latin 5. Vulgate 6. Anglo-Saxon 7. The first and last letters of the Greek alphabet

Missing vowels (page 29)
1. Ezra 2. Esther 3. Ecclesiastes 4. Isaiah 5. Hosea 6. Ezekiel 7. Amos 8. Obadiah

Alphabet (pages 30–31)
Andrew, Barabbas, Cornelius, Demetrius, Elizabeth, Festus, Gabriel, Herod, Iscariot, King, Lazarus, Martha, Nicodemus, Onesimus, Peter, Quartus, Rhoda, Stephen, Titus, Urbanus or Urbane, Zacchaeus.

Bible code (page 31)
The grace of the Lord Jesus Christ be with your spirit. (Philippians 4.23 – RSV)

Hexagons (page 32)
1. Sirion 2. Eunice 3. Reuben 4. Hebron 5. Joshua 6. Hebrew 7. Esther

Find the books (page 33)
corn, open, love, obey, salt, star, into, acid, noon, sons. *Books:* Colossians, Revelation.

Crossword No. 9 (pages 34–35)
Across: 1. Lebanon 6. stand 9. bee 10. ear 11. voice 12. lie 13. Dan 14. needs 17. Crispus
Down: 2. bat 3. Nun 4. Babylon 5. Corinth 6. seven 7. abide 8. deeds 15. Eli 16. dip

The secret way (page 35)
'I am the way, and the truth, and the life' (John 14.6)

Crazy couples (page 36)
(A) Adam and Eve, Samson and Delilah, Ahab and Jezebel, Ananias and Sapphira, Aquila and Priscilla; (B) Cain and Abel, Jacob and Esau, Moses and Aaron, David and Jonathan, Ruth and Naomi, James and John; (C) Abraham and the Promised Land, Moses and the burning bush, Joshua and the Battle of Jericho, Elijah and the ravens, Balaam and his ass, Solomon and the Temple.

Riddle (page 36)
ANNA (Luke 2.36) add H to the beginning and end to make HANNAH (1 Samuel 1.20)

Name-search (page 37)
Philippians, Corinthians, Ephesians, Timothy, Thessalonians, Titus, Galatians, Romans, Colossians, Philemon.

Bible Code (page 37)
Grace be with all of you. Amen. (Hebrews 13.25)

Crossword No. 10 (pages 38–39)
Across: 1. Abigail 7. bar 8. lap 9. Leviticus 10. Nun 12. all 13. Abishai
Down: 2. bar 3. Galatians 4. ill 5. Abilene 6. apostle 11. Nob 12. Asa

Riddle-me-ree (page 39)
Synagogue

Apostles in hiding (page 39)
The names are found by reading the first letters of the words
1. James 2. Philip 3. Simon 4. Matthew 5. John

Crossword No. 11 (pages 40–41)
Across: 1. Jezreel 5. angel 7. Ezra 8. Adam 10. alpha 11. Bernice
Down: 2. rags 3. Genesis 4. Ishmael 5. Adria 6. Lydia 9. span

Riddle-me-ree (page 41)
Caesar

What does it mean? (page 41)

1. 'Little girl, I say to you, arise.' (RSV) ('Damsel I say unto thee arise.' AV) 2. Given to God (RSV) (a gift (AV)) 3. Be opened 4. Place of the skull 5. My God, my God, why hast thou forsaken me?

Name-spiral (pages 42–43)

1. Tarshish 2. Shama 3. Malachi 4. Hiram 5. Amminadab 6. Abana 7. Naomi 8. Michael 9. Elijah 10. Ahab 11. Abraham 12. Amasa 13. Samuel 14. Elizabeth 15. Thessalonica 16. Carmel 17. Elisha 18. Ham 19. Ammonites 20. Esther 21. Erastus

Earning their livings (page 43)

1. High Priest 2. Tentmaker 3. Farmer 4. Centurion 5. Silversmith 6. Hunter 7. Roman Governor 8. Physician (doctor) 9. Seller of purple goods 10. Commander of the Syrian army 11. Slave 12. Tentmaker.

Hexagons (page 44)

1. Sinner 2. Josiah 3. Naaman 4. Romans 5. Borrow 6. Samson 7. Sorrow

Mini-quiz: parables (page 45)

1. The good Samaritan 2. The prodigal son 3. The fig-tree 4. Jericho 5. The lost coin 6. The lost sheep 7. Lazarus 8. The house built on a rock. 9. The sower 10. The mustard seed 11. The publican 12. The leaven

Crossword No. 12 (pages 46–47)

Across: 1. Titus 5. few 7. Asa 8. inn 9. ten 11. Simon 13. Syria 16. ant 18. Nun 19. eat 20. Dan 22. music
Down: 2. the 3. Isaac 4. Kings 5. fat 6. win 10. ear 12. man 14. Abner 15. enter 16. and 17. ten 21. ass

Crossword No. 13 (pages 48–49)
Across: 1. ram 3. axe 4. ark 6. air 7. ship 9. sins
12. none 15. skin 17. vow 18. eye 19. Asa 20. run
Down: 1. reap 2. Mars 3. ash 5. kin 7. son 8. inn
10. ink 11. sun 13. one 14. ever 15. swan 16. Ira

A hidden message (page 50)
The letters are drawn using only vertical and horizontal
lines, no curves or diagonals, rather like a computer
alphabet. Also every second letter is upside down. The
message is: 'In the beginning God created the heavens
and the earth.' It is the first verse in the Bible. (Genesis
1.1)

The secret way 2 (page 51)
'A new commandment I give to you, that you love one
another; even as I have loved you, that you also love
one another.' (John 13.34 – RSV)

Mini-quiz: the twelve apostles (page 51)
1. Zebedee 2. Simon 3. Simon 4. James and John
5. Judas Iscariot

Crossword No. 14 (pages 52–53)
Across: 2. Sheba 4. lap 5. Bel 7. evangelists 11. Meso-
potamia 16. Eve 17. Ain 18. Bamah
Down: 1. Deuteronomy 2. span 3. Abdi 4. Lev 6. Lot
7. elm 8. ass 9. Sam 10. sea 12. Eve 13. Oreb 14. Adah
15. inn

More anagrams (page 53)
1. Ezra 2. Esther 3. Daniel 4. Romans 5. Leviticus
6. Samuel 7. Lamentations 8. Hosea 9. Matthew
10. Hebrews

Crossword No. 15 (pages 54–55)
Across: 1. Job 3. son 4. ink 6. all 7. Sarah 9. death
12. noise 15. never 17. awe 18. air 19. sow 20. his
Down: 1. Jonah 2. build 3. Sur 5. Koa 7. sun 8. ass
10. Eve 11. Hur 13. Ira 14. earth 15. nests 16. vow

Book-search (page 56)
Isaiah, Jeremiah, Lamentations, Ezekiel, Daniel, Hosea,
Joel, Amos, Obadiah, Jonah, Micah, Nahum, Habakkuk, Zephaniah, Haggai, Zechariah, Malachi. (They
are the prophetic books of the Old Testament)

Hexagons (page 57)
1. Shunem 2. Sharon 3. narrow 4. Emmaus 5. Peniel
6. mother 7. Pithom

Mini-quiz: miracles (page 58)
1. Simon 2. Lazarus 3. a centurion 4. paralysis or palsy
5. Jairus 6. twelve years 7. Cana 8. a servant of the high
priest 9. the Sabbath 10. the sea

Crossword No. 16 (pages 59–60)
Across: 1. sting 3. never 5. Matthew 7. seats 8. males
9. round 11. drive 13. evening 14. hours 15. Kings
Down: 1. spots 2. gates 3. Nahum 4. roots 5. measure
6. walking 9. rough 10. dregs 11. drink 12. evils

Riddle-me-ree (page 60)
Deuteronomy

Crossword No. 17 (pages 61–62)
Across: 1. Annas 4. beard 7. ink 8. Michmas 9. tables
10. Shur 12. Baal 14. cherub 17. Lebanon 18. Lot
19. Silas 20. Mered

Down: 1. Aristobulus 2. Nekeb 3. Samuel 4. back 5. Admah 6. distributed 11. Shunem 13. Arbel 15. ruler 16. ants

Crossword No. 18 (pages 63–64)
Across: 1. Babel 4. Isaac 7. latin 8. David 9. Uri 10. Kings 12. Abner 14. hymns 17. snare 20. Eli 21. Spain 22. Magog 23. Asher 24. noble
Down: 1. Balak 2. Beten 3. Linus 4. India 5. Alvan 6. cedar 11. Gen 13. Ben 14. Hosea 15. Maath 16. Senir 17. Simon 18. Argob 19. eagle

Strangers (page 65)
The set to which the rest of the group belong is mentioned in the brackets following the name of the 'stranger'.
1. Scorpion (birds) 2. Locust (trees) 3. Syrians (New Testament letters) 4. Jerusalem (Greek towns) 5. Isaac (prophetic books) 6. Paul (evangelists or gospels) 7. The Widow's Mite (parables) 8. Nazarites (gentile races or tribes) 9. Damascus (Judean towns) 10. Joel (sons of Jacob or tribes of Israel) 11. Jordan (mountains) 12. Egypt (all the other names refer to the same country) 13. Centimetre (Biblical measures of length) 14. Barabbas (apostles) 15. Titus (Old Testament books) 16. Jonathan (kings) 17. Colossians (Old Testament books) 18. Stephen (companions of St Paul)

Crossword No. 19 (pages 66–67)
Across: 1. Psalm 3. seven 5. Herodians 8. Rumah 9. tents 10. thrust out 11. flint 13. Amasa 15. earnestly 16. Sarah 17. reign
Down: 1. Peter 2. myrrh 3. shaft 4. names 5. Hamathite 6. dum stone 7. sanctuary 11. flies 12. Terah 13. altar 14. Amnon

Crossword No. 20 (pages 68–69)

Across: 1. Terah 7. Senate 8. Sinai 9. talent 10. Damaris
15. Susanna 16. Sardis 17. Salem 18. pastor. 19. Amasa
Down: 2. Elijah 3. Ararat 4. Demas 5. raven 6. tents
9. Titus 11. Balaam 12. angels 13. Asaph 14. arise
15. Sidon

Anagrams again (pages 69–70)
1. Nebo 2. Babylon 3. Acts 4. locust 5. adder 6. mole
7. Zebedee 8. Delilah 9. Thomas 10. Ruth 11. Daniel
12. Philemon 13. Nile 14. snail 15. Eden 16. Stephen
17. Revelation 18. Andrew 19. Ezra 20. Manasseh
21. Elisha 22. horse 23. Psalms 24. Amos 25. Onesimus
26. goat

Mini-quiz: brothers (page 71)
Abel, Esau, Moses, Andrew, James

Bible code (page 71)
'Peace to all of you that are in Christ.' (1 Peter 5.14 –
RSV)

Crossword No. 21 (pages 72–73)
Across: 1. Corinthians 7. lambs 8. noise 9. Ehud
10. waters 13. Hoshea 14. heal 17. shade 19. Orion
20. Aristobulus
Down: 1. Chloe 2. rumours 3. nest 4. Hannah 5. Ahi
6. steps 11. Ezekiel 12. reject 13. Hosea 15. lines 16. Joab
18. Ami

Crossword No. 22 (pages 74–75)
Across: 1. Zimri 4. Salem 7. Resen 8. Nabal 9. and
11. head 13. Dara 14. Adoni 15. Cain 17. Eden 20. Zia
22. Lahmi 23. Magog 24. Syria 25. Senir

Down: 1. Zorah 2. Massa 3. Imna 4. sand 5. Libya 6. Melea 10. Naomi 12. Dan 13. die 15. colts 16. Ibhar 18. Dagon 19. Niger 20. Ziza 21. Amos

Anagrams: people Paul knew (page 76)
1. Stephen 2. Ananias 3. Barnabas 4. Silas 5. Timothy 6. Lydia 7. Apollos 8. Erastus 9. Titus 10. Demetrius

For the Code-breakers (page 77)
It is like a grain of mustard seed which a man took and sowed in his garden; and it grew and became a tree, and the birds of the air made nests in its branches. (Luke 13.19 RSV)

Mini-quiz: the Psalms (page 77)
1. 150 2. 119 3. 176 4. 23 5. Song or hymn 6. 117 7. Hebrew 8. Alfred the Great.

Crossword No. 23 (pages 78–79)
Across: 1. Jacob 4. Naomi 7. Salma 8. India 9. Zin 11. Edom 13. true 14. Ammah 15. bear 17. Esau 20. cry 22. Shiza 23. Adami 24. melon 25. needy
Down: 1. Jesse 2. Calno 3. Boaz 4. Nain 5. order 6. image 10. Immer 12. Mar 13. the 15. bosom 16. Ariel 18. shame 19. unity 20. Cain 21. yarn

Cogwheels (pages 80–81)
1. Amos 2. Moab 3. Abel 4. Nebo 5. Boaz 6. tool 7. Baal 8. Obal 9. moon 10. beam 11. star 12. Anna 13. born 14. root 15. stay 16. Ezra 17. span 18. rags 19. hart 20. sent 21. hell 22. Paul 23. Agag 24. Ahab 25. pant

Hidden creatures (page 81)

1. Owl, bat, dove. 2. Frog, goat, dog. 3. Ass, hen, gnat. 4. Camel, ant, bee.

Crossword No. 24 (pages 82–83)

Across: 1. Deuteronomy 9. Aaron 10. Telah 11. his 13. ten 14. Bunah 16. all 17. err 18. wet 20. olive 21. sheep 22. ear 24. bee 25. one 27. dined 29. Ahi 30. big 31. evils 33. crown 34. Canaanitess

Down: 2. Ekron 3. ten 4. rezin 5. net 6. Melea 7. Bartholomew 8. Philippians 11. Hur 12. saw 14. bread 15. Hesed 17. Eve 19. the 23. rib 24. beg 26. Elika 28. Nisan 29. aloes 32. sea 33. cut